PRODUCTION: PLAYDAYS 1997

Take 1

This book belongs to:

_____

_____

_____

message:

Hello to all our readers!
We hope you enjoy all the fun-packed pages in this annual.
Best wishes from all your friends at Playdays.

The annual is based on the BBC television programme Playdays produced by Felgate Media Ltd. for BBC television.
The BBC logotype and the Playdays logotype are trademarks of the British Broadcasting Corporation.
"BBC" and "Playdays" are registered trademarks of the British Broadcasting Corporation.
All trademarks are used under non-exclusive licence.

Text © Felgate Media Ltd., 1996

Written and designed by Philippa Blake and additional material by Clare Bradley

Illustrated by Kristina Stephenson, Paul Johnson, Sonia Canals, Angela Jolliffe and Jeannette Slater

Stories by Jan Page, Arabella Warner and Michele Durler

Published in Great Britain by World International Limited, Deanway Technology Centre, Wilmslow Road, Handforth, Cheshire SK9 3FB

4

Contents

Come dance with me!

Note to adults
The emphasis in this book is for joint activities involving both children and adults. We offer some suggestions on how selective pages might be used, but we are sure you will have lots of ideas of your own.

The Patch Stop Photo Album

Peggy's friend Sarah.

A puffin.

This man is called a piper. He is playing an instrument called bagpipes.

Peggy on the Isle of Barra in Scotland.

Hello, my name is Peggy Patch!

Stick a photograph of yourself here or you can draw a picture if you don't have a photograph.

Peggy's special friend

Peggy's den.

Mark showing Peggy a baby swan. It's called a cygnet.

Poppy painting a picture.

Peggy exploring in the ferns.

Peggy watching Why bird and Poppy arriving by plane on the beach.

Peggy and a flower.

Peggy's nature trail
Look! Some eggs have been laid on this leaf. Can you guess what they will grow into? Turn to page 18 to find out.

7

Poppy's dressing-up box

Can you colour in these clothes, choose colours that match the labels.

brown

pink

blue

green

red

Ha-ha, my hearty!

Dressing up is a good vehicle for self expression.

A chat with Mr Jolly

Hello, Mr Jolly!

name: Mr Jolly
best friend: Rosie the Roundabout
favourite colour: yellow
favourite clothes: my bowler hat
favourite food: roly poly pudding
best sport: making people laugh
favourite flower: a Rosie rose
favourite place: The Roundabout Stop

Do you have a hobby?
Yes, telling jokes. But I'd also like to make the puppet on page 22.

Mr. Jolly x

9

Going Filming

Can you find all the items in the picture?
As you find them, tick the boxes.

Make-up

Wardrobe

Poppy

why

Peggy

script

ST. JOHN'S
RECREATION
GROUND

10

13

Labelling
with Poppy and Karl

Where should the labels go?

Poppy　**Karl**

chair	television	fruit

door	Why	book

Peggy	lamp	Mr Jolly

 Why not put labels on items in your home, or place names at the dinner table?

 15

Odd letter out game

Can you find the odd letter in each set?

A small caterpillar or larva hatches from each egg. During its life it will change its skin several times. Each time it will grow larger and more colourful. Turn to page 34 to find out what happens next.

18

Spot the differences with Why

Four things are missing in picture 2. Can you spot them?

 Look at what Why has filed on each shelf. Has she put the things in the right department?

A trip to the cinema

 has some  for his friends.  has  to buy  and a  . The  is so funny that  laughs **ha-ha** and falls off his  .  drinks all her  and

now needs the  .

 likes the  best.

 is sad when the

ends, so  takes them to

 for

and  .

Now  is happy again.

Who do you like best in the video?
Can you draw a picture of them?

Make a puppet with Charlie Grindle

Paper bag puppet

You will need: Brown paper bag, felt tip pens, a wooden spoon, elastic bands, sticky tape, an old newspaper.

1. Draw a face on the paper bag.

2. Twist the corners for ears.

3. Stuff the bag with crunched up newspaper into the centre of the bag to fill it out.

Eooww! It's Poppy Puppet!

4. Insert the wooden spoon.

5. secure the neck with elastic bands or sticky tape.

22

We have used sticky tape and stickers where possible in order for the spoons to be returned to the kitchen after the show.

Wooden spoon puppet

You will need:
wooden spoon, assorted stickers
felt tip pens, wool scraps or newspaper,
sticky tape, scraps of fabric, ribbon.

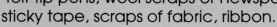

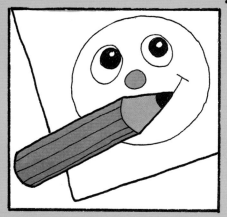

1. Draw a face onto a large sticker.

2. Put the sticker onto the spoon.

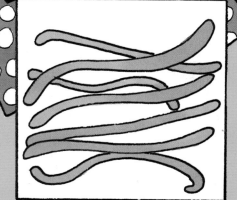

3. Cut lengths of wool or newspaper.

4. Tie the centre of the strands together for hair.

5. Sticky tape the parting of the hair to the spoon.

6. Cut a square of fabric. Cut a small cross in the centre of the fabric.

7. Push the handle through the cross.

8. Secure the neck of the spoon and fabric together with sticky tape and tie the ribbon over the top.

9. By cutting a further triangle of fabric you can make different hats.

A chat with Dave

Hello, Dave!

name:	Dave Benson Phillips
best friends:	Chester and Lizzie
favourite colour:	red
favourite shirt:	the one I'm wearing in this picture
favourite food:	the coconut Barfi on page 56
best sport:	Swimming
favourite flower:	Poppy
favourite place:	my home

Do you have a hobby?
Yes, juggling. It's great fun.

Dave Benson Phillips

The runaway glove
by Jan Page

For Christmas Harry was given a new pair of gloves. He liked the look of the gloves, but he didn't like wearing them very much. He liked to run about and pick things up with his hands and his gloves got in the way, so he shoved them in his pockets.

Harry's gloves didn't like living in his anorak pocket. It was boring, stuck in the dark with nothing to see and nothing to do.

"I want to see a bit of the world," thought the Left Glove. "I'm going to escape!"

She waited until Harry next went out to play in the garden and when Harry wasn't looking, the Left Glove wriggled and wriggled and squiggled until *Plop!* She fell quietly onto the ground. Freedom at last!

Harry went indoors for his lunch and the Glove waited for her adventures to begin.

The weather was getting colder. The wind started to blow and the Glove felt herself being lifted into the air. "I can fly!" she shouted. "Look at me everybody, I can fly and dance in the sky!"

The wind carried the Left Glove out of the garden and suddenly dropped her on to the pavement. "Careful!" cried the Glove. "You don't have to be so rough, Wind!"

The Left Glove watched people walking up and down the street. She saw a lady carrying some very heavy shopping. She saw a dad pushing his baby in a pram. She saw an old man walking his dog. The dog came up very close and gave the Glove a sniff with his wet nose.

Then a boy came up and started to kick the Left Glove along the street. "Oh, no!" cried the Glove. "I'm not a football!"

"Goal!" shouted the boy as he kicked the Left Glove into the gutter. And then to her relief he ran away.

She lay in the gutter gasping for breath. It was very cold and starting to get frosty and dark. The Glove started to wish she was back in Harry's pocket. She missed her brother, the Right Glove. She didn't like being on her own, she wanted to be part of a pair again.

In the morning the old man came back, taking his dog for his morning walk. The dog gave the Left Glove another big sniff with his wet nose.

"Oh dear, someone has lost their glove," said the old man, bending down to pick up the Left Glove. "You're about to be needed," he said to the Glove. "It's about to snow." And the old man shook the frost from the glove's fingers and hung it on the garden fence.

Later that morning it did start to snow. Harry went into the garden to throw snowballs, but his hands quickly grew frozen and numb.

Suddenly he remembered his new gloves. "They'll keep me warm," he thought. He reached into his pockets but instead of a pair there was only one — one lonely right glove.

"Oh, no — I've lost one — one of my new gloves!"

Then just as he turned to go indoors, something caught his eye. At the end of the garden it looked as if someone was waving. It was his missing glove!

He rushed over and put both his gloves on straightaway.

"I'm so glad you're back!" whispered the Right Glove to the Left. "I really missed you."

"I missed you too," replied the Left Glove. "I promise I'll never run away again."

And the Gloves went off with Harry to enjoy a great game of snowballs.

Lizzyrella is late for the ball!

Can you help me?

Can you join the dots?
Can you colour in Lizzy's dress?

 Trace over the pattern with your finger before using a pen.

 31

The dressing up department

Poppy, Peggy and Why love dressing up. Can you spot the clothes they choose?

A sparkly dress down to the ground,
Some high-heeled shoes,
A cloak,
A crown.
Can you guess what I'm going to be?
Yes — Princess Poppy —that's me!

32

A pair of eyes that boing on springs,
A fat green body,
Some paper wings.
Can you guess what I'm going to be?
Yes — Peggy the alien monster — that's me!

A spotty scarf tied on one side,
A golden earring,
And a patch on my eye.
Can you guess what I'm going to be?
Yes — Whybeard the pirate — that's me!

What would you dress up as?

To be read aloud. Encourage the listener to find the items mentioned, both on the character and around the picture.

Mr Jolly makes play dough

You will need:
10 oz/ 300 grams/2 cups of plain flour
8 fl oz/ 1 cup of cold water to mix
5 oz/ 150 grams/ 1 cup of salt
1 tablespoon of cooking oil
non-toxic powder paint
a wooden spoon
a mixing bowl

Happy modelling!

1. Put the flour, salt and cooking oil in the mixing bowl.

2. Mix the powder paint in with the water.

3. Add the colour into the dough gradually.

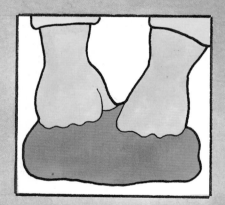

4. Knead for 3 to 4 minutes.

5. Have fun modelling.

6. Keep the dough in an airtight container in the fridge.

Slowly the caterpillar turns into a pupa or chrysalis and then attaches itself to a plant stalk.
Turn to page 36 for what happens next.

Safe tools to use when modelling: plastic knives, cookie cutters, garlic crusher, rolling pins.

At the circus!

Your Playdays friends are playing together.
Can you see what they are doing in the picture?
What do you think will happen next?
Turn to page 37 to find out.

Encourage the reader to use words such as:
up, on, over, by and in when describing this picture and the outcome on page 37.

35

Spot the odd one out!

Can you spot the Playdays bus?

Now the pupa splits open.
Can you guess what comes out?
Turn to page 62 for the answer.

Later at the Circus!

Can you see what has happened?

The giant turnip

retold by Arabella Warner

Once upon a time there was an old woman. She had one turnip seed which she planted in the ground. Then she waited to see how well it would grow.

After a while the seed grew into a small turnip, then a medium sized turnip, then a large turnip and at last into a gigantic turnip!

"Now it's ready to pull up and eat," said the old woman, so she took hold of the turnip and she pulled.

She pulled and she pulled and she pulled, until she could pull no longer but the turnip just would not come out of the ground.

So the old woman asked the farmer, who was working in the next field, to help her. "Please Farmer, could you help me pull my turnip?"

So the farmer took hold of the old woman and the old woman took hold of the turnip and they pulled.

They pulled and they pulled and they pulled, until they could pull no longer. But still the turnip would not come out of the ground.

Just at that moment the postman passed by and so the old woman asked him to help her. "Please Postman, will you help me pull my turnip?"

So the postman took hold of the farmer and the farmer took hold of the old woman and the old woman took hold of the turnip and they all pulled.

They pulled and they pulled and they pulled, until they could pull no longer but still the turnip would not come out of the ground.

39

Then the old woman spotted a policewoman and asked her to help her. "Please Policewoman, will you help me pull my turnip?"

So the policewoman took hold of the postman and the postman took hold of the farmer and the farmer took hold of the old woman and the old woman took hold of the turnip and they pulled.

They pulled and they pulled and they pulled, until they could pull no longer but still the turnip would not come out of the ground.

Just then the milkman came by and the old woman asked him to help. "Please Milkman, will you help me pull my turnip?"

So the milkman took hold of the policewoman and the policewoman took hold of the postman and the postman took hold of the farmer and the farmer took hold of the old woman and the old woman took hold of the turnip and they pulled.

They pulled and they pulled and they pulled, until they could pull no longer but still the turnip did not come out of the ground.

Then a teacher came by on her way to school and the

old woman asked her to help. "Please Teacher, will you help me pull my turnip?"

So the teacher took hold of the milkman and the milkman took hold of the policewoman and the policewoman took hold of the postman and the postman took hold of the farmer and the farmer took hold of the old woman and the old woman took hold of the turnip and they pulled.

They pulled and they pulled and they pulled, until they could pull no longer and the turnip **did** come out of the ground!

The turnip came out so suddenly that it fell on the old woman, the old woman fell on the farmer, the farmer fell on the postman, the postman

fell on the policewoman, the policewoman fell on the milkman and the milkman fell on the teacher!

And they all dragged and they heaved and they pulled the gigantic turnip back to the old woman's house, where she cut it up, put it in a huge pot of water and made it into soup. And do you know, there was so much soup that they are still eating it?

The lost hat

Can you help
Mr Jolly find
his hat?

 Encourage the player to follow the maze with a finger and to imagine what Mr Jolly would look like in the other hats.

Why's words

P

Can you tick the things that start with p?

pineapple
Peggy
pizza
pirate
Poppy
peg
penguin
pencil
pig

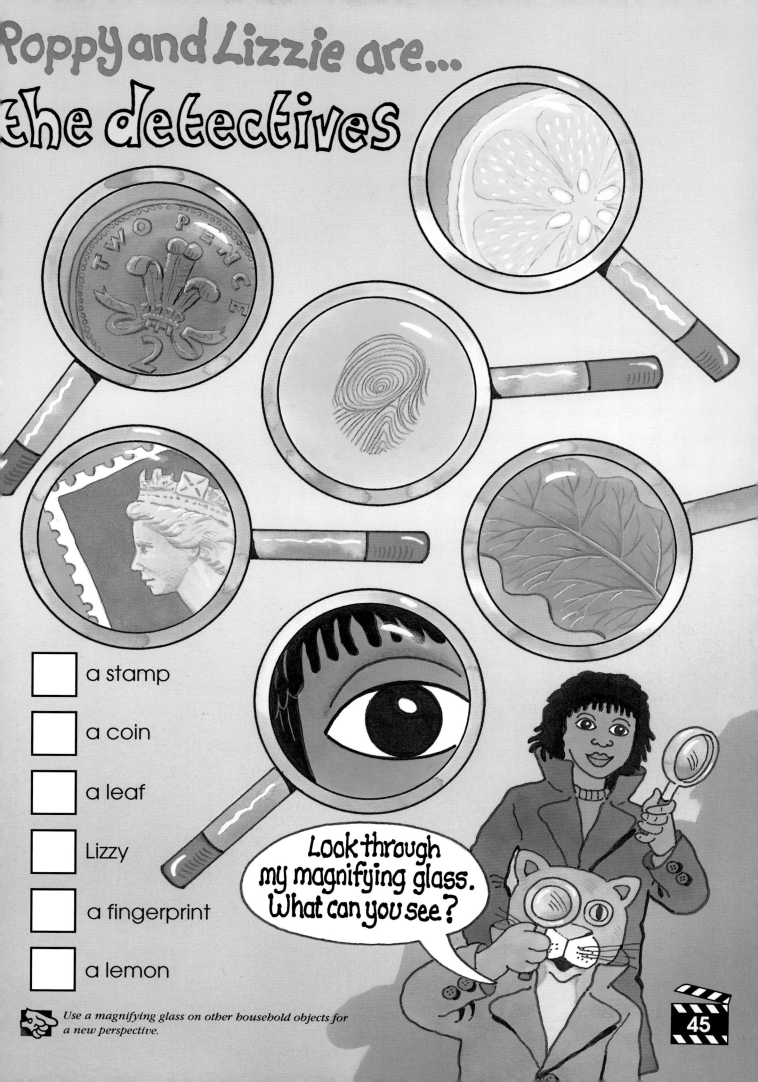

You can dress up

Here are some ideas.
Can you think of any more?

a costume

Take a large piece
of material or
paper with a hole
cut out.

Paint it all over
with monster
colours.

Make sure
it's dry before you
wear it!

a wig

Take long strips of
newspaper
or other paper.

Bind with tape.

This can be fixed onto
a hat or elastic.

46

as a monster!

Wear some socks on your hands!

hands and feet

Wear some gloves on your feet!

You could tape on some claws cut out of card.

Stuff the fingers with newspaper!

some extra eyes

Use half a cardboard egg box.

Paint like eyeballs and fix on elastic.

make up

If you have some face paints you could experiment with monster faces.

Just a few ideas to get you going. What you do is dependent on time available and what you have around the house.

1

2

3

4

A8

A9

A10

BI

At the cinema

 48 5

6

We went to the cinema for a treat.
We each had a ticket for our seat.
There were lots of stalls selling hot dogs and ices,
And popcorn at different sizes and prices.
We had to go in to Screen Number 3,
But inside it was dark — we could hardly see.
So a man with a torch showed us where we
should go.
"Seats 8, 9 and 10 at the end of this row."
Well the film was fantastic, and we can't
wait till when
We can visit the cinema once again.

10

9

7

8

49

The weather house

by Michele Durler

There was once a little weather house which sat way up high on a dusty shelf by a window. Although two people lived in the house, neither of them knew that the other one existed!

When it poured with rain, Sam Showers would come out to splash around in the puddles.

"I do love it when it rains," said Sam. "It's so much fun in the rain. I don't like the sunshine though — oh no, I stay indoors when the sun comes out and I wait for the weather to change. Sometimes I wait indoors for days!"

Whenever it was sunny, Sally Sunshine would come out to sunbathe.

"I do love it when it's sunny," said Sally. "It's so much fun in the sun. I don't like it when it starts to rain though — oh no, I stay indoors when it rains and I wait for the weather to change. Sometimes I wait indoors for days!"

So, in all the years that Sally Sunshine and Sam Showers had lived in their little weather house they had never met!

One day, it began to snow. Neither of them liked the snow. It snowed for hours. It snowed for days and then weeks. Sally and Sam sat in their doorways hoping the snow would go away.

"Go away, snow! Hurry up, rain!" Sam thought to himself. "I'm very bored and I'm getting rather lonely."

Weeks later the snow finally stopped. Sam and Sally waited eagerly in their doorways wondering whether it would be rainy or sunny.

"Please, please let it rain, so I can go and play in the puddles," said Sam.

"Please, please let it be sunny, so I can go and sunbathe and eats lots of ice cream," said Sally.

Then, all of a sudden, something very strange happened. The rain began to pour and at the very same time, the sun began to shine!

"Hooray! The rain!" said Sam.

"Hooray! The sun!" said Sally.

And Sally Sunshine and Sam Showers came rushing out of the little house at the same time!

"Hello! Who are you?" said Sam.

"I'm Sally Sunshine — I come out when the sun is shining. Who are you?"

"I'm Sam Showers — I come out when it rains. How exciting that we're both out together. I never knew you lived next door."

And Sam and Sally talked and talked. And played together in the puddles and ate lots of yummy ice cream. Infact, they nearly missed the beautiful rainbow that had appeared in the sky!

"Look, Sally! A rainbow!" said Sam. "I've never seen one of those before. We should come out together more often!"

And Sam Showers and Sally Sunshine were never lonely again because they knew they had a friend living next door. And every day, they would look out for the rainbow so they could go and play together again.

Make coconut barfi
with Dave and Why Bird

What you will need:

A mixing bowl, wooden spoon
and a small sugar bowl or mug
* see note

Coconut Barfi
1 bowl or mug of caster sugar
a little milk
1 bowl or mug of milk powder
2 bowls or mugs of dessicated coconut

Topping
3tablespoons of icing sugar
1 tablespoon of cocoa
1 tablespoon of drinking chocolate
2 tablespoons of milk

Put 1 mug of caster sugar and a little milk in a mixing bowl.

Mix with a wooden spoon into a thick paste.

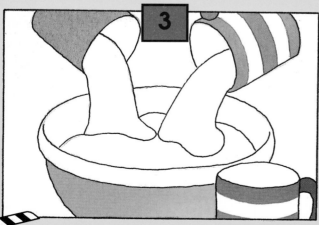

Add 1 mug of milk powder and 2 mugs of dessicated coconut.

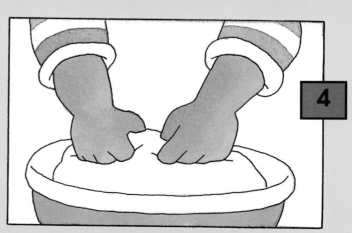

Mix to a thick dough.
(Add more milk if necessary)

5 Can I eat it now? Not yet, why!

Spread the mixture flat on a plate.

6 Mix all the topping ingredients to a smooth paste.

7 Spread the topping on the coconut mixture.

8 Put the plate in the fridge for an hour.

9 Break into small pieces and serve.

Ahh-ha! A clue! Turn to page 63.

In this recipe the measurements are done by the bowl or mug. Supervision is necessary in all cooking and a lot of patience.

57

Which hat?

Can you spot the hat for everyone's costume?

Can the player guess what each character is dressed up as and identify the correct hat to complete the outfit. Who might wear the other hats?

59

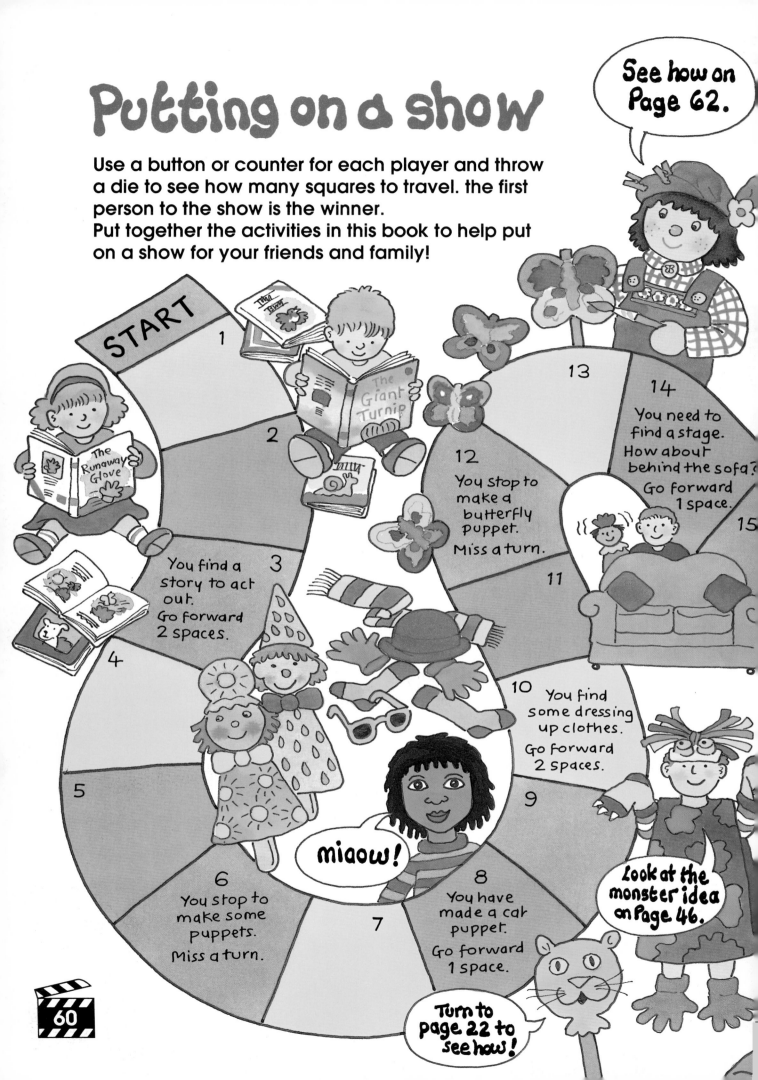

The trail ends

Wow! It's a butterfly. It won't take long for this female to lay her own eggs and start the story all over again.
Isn't nature brilliant?

Butterfly activity

Fold a piece of paper in half (side to side) open it and drop big blobs of runny paint on one side. Fold the clean half of the paper onto the paint and press outwards before opening it again to reveal a magical butterfly.

Butterfly puppet

Back the paper with card and cut it into a butterfly shape. Finally attach a wooden spoon or a stick to the card with sticky tape.

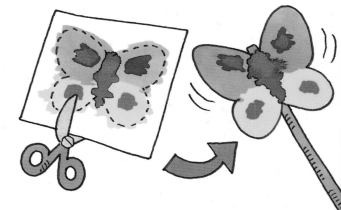